English Practice Year 4

Question Book

Giles Clare

Name _____

Schofield & Sims

Introduction

The **Schofield & Sims English Practice Year 4 Question Book** uses step-by-step practice to develop children's understanding of key English concepts. It covers every Year 4 objective in the 2014 National Curriculum programme of study.

The structure

This book is split into units, which are based on the key areas of the English curriculum for Year 4. These are:

- Grammar
- Punctuation
- Spelling
- Vocabulary
- Reading comprehension.

Each double-page spread follows a consistent 'Practise', 'Extend' and 'Apply' sequence designed to deepen and reinforce learning. Each objective also includes a 'Remember' box that reminds children of the key information needed to help answer the questions.

There are three reading comprehension units in this book. Each reading comprehension unit is linked by an overarching theme and includes a fiction, non-fiction and poetry text. Each text is accompanied by a set of comprehension questions, which practise reading skills such as inference, retrieval, summarising, prediction and analysis of word choice.

Additionally, a 'Writing skills' section allows children to apply the skills they have developed throughout the book in an extended writing task. The writing task is inspired by the themes covered in the reading comprehension texts and gives opportunities for children to showcase their creative writing.

At the back of the book, there is a 'Final practice' section. Here, mixed questions are used to check children's understanding of the knowledge and skills acquired throughout the book and identify any areas that need to be revisited.

A mastery approach

The **Primary Practice English** series follows a knowledge-based mastery approach. The books have a focus on learning with purpose to improve children's ability across all areas of English and to link learning in grammar, punctuation, spelling, vocabulary, reading and writing. There is frequent, varied practice and application of concepts to improve children's confidence when using their skills. A strong emphasis is given to vocabulary enrichment, reading for pleasure and reading stamina.

Assessment and checking progress

A 'Final practice' section is provided at the end of this book to check progress against the Year 4 English objectives. Children are given a target time of 45 minutes to complete this section, which is marked out of 30. Once complete, it enables them to assess their new knowledge and skills independently and to see the areas where they might need more practice.

Online answers

Answers for every question in this book are available to download from the **Schofield & Sims** website. The answers are accompanied by detailed explanations where helpful. There is also a progress chart, allowing children to track their learning as they complete each set of questions, and an editable certificate.

Contents

Nouns and pronouns

Remember

Pronouns are words that replace nouns. They refer to someone or something earlier in the sentence and stop writing from becoming repetitive. For example: '**Samuel** likes cooking, but **Samuel** doesn't like to bake' can change to '**Samuel** likes cooking, but **he** doesn't like to bake'.

 Practise

(1) Underline the pronoun in each sentence. In some sentences there may be more than one.

a. Ada went to the fairground, but <u>she</u> was too scared to go on the rides.

b. Dad and I went to the beach while <u>we</u> were on holiday in Spain.

c. Alex and Mum lost the map, but <u>they</u> managed to find the way home.

d. You and I are going to the cinema all <u>by</u> <u>ourselves</u>.

e. He stared at <u>himself</u> in the mirror.

(2) Write the correct pronoun to complete each sentence. Use each word once.

> ~~she~~   ~~he~~   ~~we~~   ~~our~~   ~~it~~

a. Bethan was excited about the picnic until _____*she*_____ realised her umbrella was at home.

b. Ryan and I studied hard for _____*our*_____ maths test.

c. Dad hates spiders. _____*he*_____ ran away when he saw one.

d. Marek had a bad dream last night. No matter what he did, he couldn't forget about _____*it*_____.

e. Although our choir had the youngest singers, _____*we*_____ won first prize in the competition.

Extend

3 Circle the noun or noun phrase that the underlined pronoun refers to.

   a. <u>Amina</u> likes video games, but <u>she</u> prefers watching films.

   b. I gave my friend a <u>peach</u> for her lunch, and <u>she</u> really enjoyed <u>it</u>.

   c. <u>Tom and Zoe</u> fell overboard and found <u>themselves</u> on a desert island.

4 Write the correct pronoun to complete each sentence. Use each word once.

> ~~themselves~~   ~~you~~   ~~it~~   ~~we~~   ~~they~~

   a. Would ___you___ like some toast and jam for your breakfast?

   b. ___they They___ are going to our favourite hotel again this summer.

   c. The pupils helped ___themselves___ to extra helpings of the delicious chocolate pudding.

   d. ___(It's)___ it's sunny this morning, but ___we___ say it might rain later.

Apply

5 Rewrite the underlined part of each sentence. Replace the nouns or noun phrases with the correct pronouns.

   a. My dad asked my sister Emily to get ready, <u>but my sister Emily started crying</u>.

   My dad asked my sister Emily to get ready, ___but she started crying___.

   b. When Yan bought a new plant at a garden centre, <u>Yan left the plant in Yan's car and the plant died</u>.

   When Yan bought a new plant at a garden centre, ___he left the plant in his car and it died___.

Possessive pronouns

Remember

Possessive pronouns show who owns something. They can be used as a determiner before a noun, for example: 'That is **my** book', or to replace the noun or noun phrase, for example: 'That is **mine**'. The possessive pronoun 'mine' shows that the book belongs to me.

 Practise

1 Circle the possessive pronouns in the cloud.

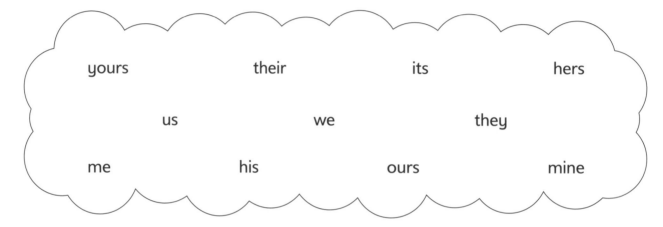

yours   their   its   hers

us   we   they

me   his   ours   mine

Tip Try using the pronouns in the example sentences in the **Remember** box to see if they make sense.

2 Circle the correct possessive pronouns in each sentence.

a. Give me some of **your / yours** food and I'll give you some of **my / mine**.

b. Those pencils are **their / theirs**, but you could borrow **our / ours**.

c. **Your / Yours** is much better than his, but not as good as **her / hers**.

d. The bird pecked **my / mine** finger because it was protecting **it's / its** eggs.

e. **My / Mine** friend told me the laptop was **him / his**.

Tip Possessive pronouns do not use apostrophes. 'Hers' and 'yours' are not spelt 'her's' and 'your's'.

▷▷ Extend

3 Write the correct possessive pronoun to complete each sentence pair. Use each word once.

> | ours | his | mine | yours | theirs |

a. The pencil case belongs to my brother. It is _____.

b. You bought a new printer. The printer is _____.

c. That money belongs to us. It is _____.

d. They bought a new house. The house is _____.

e. I got a new pony. The pony is _____.

4 Complete these sentences using suitable possessive pronouns.

a. _____ dog is much smaller than _____.

b. The athletes lost _____ kit, so we gave them _____.

c. _____ is a more up-to-date version of _____ phone.

d. The panther showed _____ teeth and _____ heart beat like a drum.

Apply

5 Write **two** sentences of your own using possessive pronouns from the box.

> | ours | theirs | mine | my | your | his | her | hers |

a. _____

_____

b. _____

_____

Determiners

Determiners go before nouns and noun phrases to show whether they are general or specific. For example: 'I saw **a** dog' is general, but 'I saw **the** dog' is more specific. Determiners can show amounts, for example: 'I saw **some** dogs', or they can show possession: 'I saw **your** dog'.

 Practise

1. Draw lines to match each determiner to the correct noun phrase.

some	pretty bird
several	ugly building
an	dirty water
a	new toys

Tip The determiner 'an' is used before words that start with a vowel sound.

 Extend

2. Underline the determiners in these sentences. There may be more than one.

   a. The old cat swished its tail slowly.

   b. Every week, you forget to bring your PE kit.

   c. Many children will be given a voucher for ten pounds.

   d. I want those packages delivered to my house later.

   e. Harry ate some cereal for breakfast and then had another bowl for lunch.

   f. I don't like that idea, so maybe we should think of other ideas.

(3) Write the correct determiner to complete each sentence. Use each word once.

an	the	many	every

a. Please would you pass me _____ box of tissues?

b. _____ morning, Shereen rode her bike to school.

c. The pirates were struck down by _____ ancient curse.

d. Leo had lost his front door key _____ times before.

Apply

(4) Find all **12** determiners in the word search.

K	T	H	O	S	E	S	K	C	Z
C	V	K	M	E	V	E	R	Y	F
R	H	T	H	E	I	R	H	C	O
F	N	F	Y	T	S	W	E	B	U
Y	O	U	R	Z	O	M	R	V	R
J	Q	D	U	M	M	V	S	T	A
M	Y	T	B	V	E	P	R	H	L
X	A	N	O	T	H	E	R	I	L
E	I	G	H	T	R	U	E	S	V

all	my	another	some
eight	their	every	this
four	those	her	your

Tip The words can run horizontally or vertically.

(5) Use the determiners from the word search to complete each sentence. The first letter of each determiner is given.

a. I would like a _____ taste of t _____ sweets.

b. There were e _____ bags of sweets in t _____

cupboard, but now there are only f _____ bags left.

c. E _____ year, m _____ grandma sends me

s _____ money from h _____ savings.

d. Y _____ dog has been barking at t _____ cat

a _____ night.

Fronted adverbials

Remember

An adverbial gives more detail about a verb. It tells you how, when, where or why something is happening.

A fronted adverbial comes at the beginning of a sentence. A comma is normally used after the adverbial. For example: '**One hundred years from now**, flying cars will fill our skies'.

 Practise

1. Sort these fronted adverbials into the table to show what type of information they give.

Yesterday,	Under the tree,	As quickly as possible,
Due to the accident,	Somewhere far away,	Once in a while,
Because of the heat,	Silently,	

How something happens	When something happens	Where something happens	Why something happens

2. Tick to show what the fronted adverbial says about the verb in these sentences.

Sentence	How	When	Where	Why
a. Once upon a time, there was a cruel king.				
b. In the shadows, a figure listened to the men talking.				
c. In a flash, the dog ate all the biscuits.				
d. In order to learn French, I moved to Paris.				

» Extend

(3) Write the correct fronted adverbial to complete each sentence.

> Due to rain   Last year   In the attic   Suddenly

a. _____ , Dani fell out of the boat. (how)

b. _____ , sports day has been postponed. (why)

c. _____ , Anita and Rebecca learnt to speak

Japanese. (when)

d. _____ , I found an old wooden box full of

mysterious objects. (where)

Apply

(4) Rewrite these sentences with the adverbial at the beginning of the sentence.
One has been done for you.

a. She has improved her times tables since the start of the school year.

   Since the start of the school year, she has improved her
   times tables.

b. Angela put on her thick coat, a scarf and a pair of gloves because of the cold.

   _____

   _____

c. Monty joined the football match with a huge grin.

   _____

   _____

d. A creature with six eyes and eight legs was stirring at the bottom of the lake.

   _____

   _____

Expanded noun phrases

 Practise

(1) Sort these words into the table. Decide if they are adjectives or nouns.

Mum	teacher	impatient	flock
missing	courage	delicious	irregular

Adjectives	Nouns

(2) Label the different parts of the expanded noun phrases. Write **A** for adjective, **D** for determiner, **N** for noun and **P** for prepositional phrase.

a. the small houses
   ↑   ↑   ↑
   __   __   __

b. some round, green pebbles
   ↑   ↑   ↑   ↑
   __   __   __   __

c. that amazing, breath-taking view over the lake
   ↑   ↑   ↑   ↑   ↑
   __   __   __   __   __

d. your quick, helpful decision about the problem
   ↑   ↑   ↑   ↑   ↑
   __   __   __   __   __

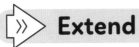

Extend

3. Write adjectives of your own to expand the noun phrases.

   a. a _____ box

   b. an _____ photo

   c. the _____ , _____ village

4. Write nouns and prepositions of your own to expand these noun phrases.

   a. our gentle, adorable _____

   b. the juicy, delicious _____

   c. that vile, horrible _____

Apply

5. Rewrite this story and expand the noun phrases to make them more interesting.

> Neela, an explorer, stared at the ground. There was a hole. She took off her hat and wiped her forehead. Sammy, her assistant, passed her a torch. Neela shone the beam, lighting up the cave. The floor seemed to be moving. Neela groaned. "Look, Sammy," she muttered. "There are dozens of frogs down there."

_____

_____

_____

_____

_____

Tip The determiner can change if the adjective or noun start with a different letter. For example, 'an engineer' becomes 'a talented engineer' because 'engineer' starts with a vowel and 'talented' starts with a consonant.

Paragraphs

Paragraphs help to organise writing. A paragraph is a group of sentences about the same theme.

Start a new paragraph when something changes. This could be when a new character or idea is introduced, when a new person speaks, or when there is a change of time or place.

 Practise

① Read the text and answer the question below.

A skeleton is a frame made of bones in humans and other mammals. In fact, there are 206 bones in the adult human skeleton. It is your skeleton that gives your body structure, helps you move and protects the organs inside you.

All bones are made of the same materials. The outer surface of a bone is a thin sheet that contains nerves and blood vessels. The next layer is smooth and very hard. Inside that, the bone looks like a sponge. This protects the layer in the very middle called bone marrow, which is like a thick jelly.

Bones might look hard and dry, but your bones are not dead. They are very much alive. They grow and change like the rest of your body. When you are born, you have around 300 bones. Over time some of them join together. By the time you are 25, all your bones have grown to full size.

It is important to look after your bones. Your skull protects your brain, so you should wear a helmet when you are on a bike. You can strengthen your bones by drinking milk or eating other foods that contain calcium.

Identify the theme of each paragraph and number them 1 to 4.

a. how bones grow   paragraph _____

b. what bones are made of   paragraph _____

c. how to care for your bones   paragraph _____

d. what the human skeleton is   paragraph _____

 **Extend**

2) Read these extra sentences. Number them 1 to 4 to show the best paragraph to add them to.

   a. You may have heard of the spine, ribs or kneecaps, which are all bones.   ————

   b. Broken bones take time to heal, so it is best to wear the right equipment when you are doing hobbies and sports.   ————

   c. Amazingly, your red blood cells are made in the middle of your bones.   ————

   d. Some bones in a baby's skeleton are made of a soft, flexible material called cartilage, which is replaced by bone as the child gets older.   ————

Apply

3) Rewrite this information about bees. Organise it into **three** paragraphs.

> There are many different types of bee in the British Isles. Social bees live in groups. Solitary bees live by themselves, in burrows underground, in old wood or even walls. Social bees are commonly seen in gardens. Honeybees may live in a group of 50 000 bees in one hive. Bumblebees live in smaller groups. A female solitary bee builds her nest and feeds her young without any help from worker bees. All these bees can be split into two main groups.

———————————————————————————————————————

———————————————————————————————————————

———————————————————————————————————————

———————————————————————————————————————

———————————————————————————————————————

———————————————————————————————————————

———————————————————————————————————————

Standard English

Standard English is the formal language that should be used in schoolwork. In Standard English, the verb agrees with the person or thing doing the action. For example: 'We **were** there', not 'We **was** there'. A double negative is non-Standard English as it uses two negative words ('I **didn't** buy **nothing**') and only one is needed in Standard English ('I **didn't** buy anything').

 Practise

1 Circle the correct verb form in each sentence.

a. They **was / were** on time for the train.

b. I **saw / seen** him the other day.

c. We **goes / went** to the cinema after school.

d. She **brung / brought** me a present out of the blue.

2 Write the correct word from the box in each sentence.

> them   these   those

a. Please could you pass me one of _____ sweets.

b. _____ trainers over here are really expensive.

c. We went to the park with _____ .

 Extend

3 Underline the double negative in each sentence. One has been done for you.

a. I <u>haven't</u> got <u>no</u> time to finish my homework.

b. He doesn't know nothing about it.

c. They don't speak to each other no more.

d. She hasn't never told me a lie.

(4) Rewrite the sentences in **Question 3** using Standard English.

a. _____

b. _____

c. _____

d. _____

(5) Rewrite the underlined word or words in each sentence. Write the word that would be used in Standard English.

a. You could <u>of</u> really hurt yourself. _____

b. <u>Ain't</u> it hot today? _____

c. I can't find <u>me</u> glasses <u>nowhere</u>. _____ _____

d. My brother is <u>gonna</u> be <u>well</u> angry. _____ _____

Apply

(6) Rewrite these sentences in Standard English.

a. Me and Joe have bought one of them scooters.

_____

b. My grandma learned me how to ride me bike.

_____

c. He don't like nobody borrowing his football.

_____

d. When we was at the park, we seen someone fall in the pond.

_____

e. She would of said something if she could of arrived in time.

_____

Inverted commas

Remember

Inverted commas (also called speech marks) show when someone is speaking. The spoken words go inside a pair of inverted commas. A reporting clause can come before, after or in the middle of the spoken words to show who is speaking. For example:

Jasmine said, "Wow! That's a lovely cat." (before)

"Wow! That's a lovely cat," **said Jasmine**. (after)

"Wow!" **said Jasmine.** "That's a lovely cat." (middle – two separate sentences of speech)

"I think," **said Jasmine,** "that your cat is lovely." (middle – one sentence of speech)

 ## Practise

1 Underline the words and punctuation that should be between inverted commas in these sentences.

a. Shut the door behind you, ordered Zeke.

b. A wise person once said, A good sleep solves most problems.

c. Don't you dare! exclaimed Lily. Those cakes aren't for you.

d. Are you serious? Frankie replied, in shock. We can't do that.

e. Excuse me, said Dad, but do you know what the time is?

2 Rewrite the sentences in **Question 1** and add inverted commas in the correct places.

a. _____

b. _____

c. _____

d. _____

e. _____

Extend

3 Write inverted commas in the correct places in these sentences.

a. I'm not surprised you are late, said Billy with a sigh.

b. The police officer explained, The road is closed after the traffic lights due to a water pipe leak.

c. Can we have our ball back? shouted Anil.

d. Don't worry, soothed Isabella. I'm sure we will find it.

Apply

4 Rewrite this conversation, adding inverted commas and other punctuation to the speech.

When is football practice asked Mandeep.

Straight after school replied his teacher Don't be late today.

Mandeep smiled and said I'm never late, Mr Barnes.

Never late I'm trying to remember said Mr Barnes any practice when you've been on time, Mandeep

How insulting exclaimed Mandeep, grinning at him.

_____

_____

_____

_____

_____

_____

Tip Remember that punctuation marks go inside inverted commas.

Possessive apostrophes

An apostrophe can show that something belongs to someone or something. For singular nouns, add **'s**. For example: 'my sister**'s** house' – the house belonging to my sister. If the word ends in 's', make sure that the apostrophe goes after the last 's' in the word. For example: 'the princess**'s** castle'; 'Thomas**'s** bicycle'.

For plural nouns that already end in 's', simply add an apostrophe. For example: 'the teachers**'** meeting'.

Practise

① Draw lines to match each phrase to its meaning.

the boy's socks	the shoes belonging to the girls
the boys' socks	the socks belonging to the boy
the girl's shoes	the shoes belonging to the girl
the girls' shoes	the socks belonging to the boys

② Tick to show which phrases use apostrophes correctly. Tick **more than one**.

my friend's trumpet ☐   hi's oldest toy ☐

the stolen present's ☐   the lorries' goods ☐

⟫ Extend

③ Underline the word that is missing an apostrophe, then write the word correctly.

a. What size are Sams feet? _____

b. The octopuss legs wrapped around my hand. _____

c. Our neighbours cat has run away from his house. _____

4 Rewrite these sentences. Remove the incorrect apostrophe and add the missing apostrophe in the correct place.

a. I love Anguss new hat and glove's, don't you?

_____

b. The mens team won their final' match.

_____

c. The cub found it's way back to the foxes den.

_____

d. We are visiting some of Spains most famous cities'.

_____

e. I was woken up by the childrens voice's.

_____

Apply

5 Write **four** sentences with different combinations of owners and possessions the table. One has been done for you.

Owner	Possession
the painter	hobbies
Lucas	parties
some people	decision
that singer	appetite
your friends	mistakes

a. The painter's hobbies included sketching and photography.

b. _____

c. _____

d. _____

Commas and clauses

Commas can be used to make sentences easier to read. When a subordinate clause comes before a main clause, use a comma to separate them. For example: 'When the pedestrian ran into the road, the van stopped suddenly'. A comma is usually not needed when the main clause comes before the subordinate clause.

Practise

(1) Tick to show which sentences need a comma. Tick **more than one**.

We went to the fair when our grandma came to stay. ☐

He will arrive on time if everything goes to plan. ☐

As we were leaving we discovered the car had a flat tyre. ☐

Peter loved football because he enjoyed playing with his friends. ☐

After school finishes today we will go to the farm. ☐

Tip Subordinating conjunctions include words like 'when', 'before', 'after', 'if', 'while', 'since' and 'because'.

Extend

(2) Circle the comma in each sentence that is in the correct place.

a. Because the , fire alarm went off , the children could not finish , the play.

b. Before , they danced in the show , they made sure , to stretch their legs.

c. Even if , the rain stops , it will , be too wet , to finish the match.

d. While the others finished , their work , I was allowed to read my book.

e. Since it will , rain today , we should postpone , our trip to the seaside.

(3) Insert a comma in the correct place in these sentences if a comma is needed. Tick to show which sentences do **not** need a comma.

While Riya waited for her friend Jack read a comic. ☐

I don't like cereal for breakfast because we have it every day. ☐

Nazir always cleaned his rugby boots after his team won a match. ☐

Every time I see you you have grown even taller. ☐

Unless he saves enough money he won't be able to buy the game. ☐

Apply

(4) Use your own ideas and the conjunction in brackets to complete these sentences.

a. She did up her coat _____

_____. (before)

b. I felt hungry _____

_____. (although)

c. _____ we win our next match _____

_____. (unless)

(5) Write **three** sentences of your own that include **one** subordinate clause and **one** main clause.

a. _____

_____

b. _____

_____

c. _____

_____

Tricky spellings

Remember

Here are some spelling rules for tricky spellings. Some words with an /s/ sound have a silent 'c': '**sc**ience'. The /ai/ sound can be spelt using 'ei', 'eigh' or 'ey': 'b**ei**ge', '**eigh**t', 'th**ey**'. Some words ending in a /g/ sound are spelt 'gue': 'lea**gue**'. Some words ending in a /k/ sound are spelt 'que': 'anti**que**'.

Practise

1 **a.** Circle the words in the cloud that are spelt correctly.

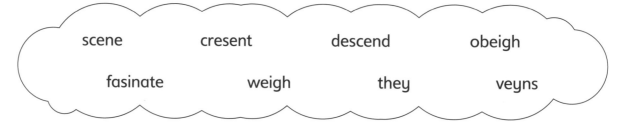

scene   cresent   descend   obeigh

fasinate   weigh   they   veyns

b. Rewrite the incorrect words in **Question 1a** using the correct spellings.

_____   _____

_____   _____

2 Complete these words using the correct ending 'gue' or 'que'.

a. anti_____   **b.** ro_____

c. uni_____   **d.** ton_____

Extend

3 Write the missing letters in each word.

a. She injured a mu __ __ le in her leg while jogging.

b. His next-door n __ __ __ __ bour knocked on the window.

c. My netball team is playing in a higher lea __ __ __ this year.

d. Light does not pass through an opa __ __ __ material.

(4) Write the correct word from the box next to its definition. Use a dictionary to help.

> plague   adolescent   mosque   prey   sceptre

a. a young person turning into an adult _____

b. a decorated stick carried by a king or queen _____

c. a serious, deadly disease _____

d. a building of worship for Muslims _____

e. an animal that is hunted for food by another animal _____

Apply

(5) **a.** Circle the **nine** incorrect spellings in this story.

"The senery here is lovely," said Sarah, the lead sientist. "But we must ascend to the top of the mountain for the best view."

"How long will it take?" her colleag Martin asked.

"About eyty minutes."

We climbed through the thick snow until fatig forced us to rest.

"We should have come on a sley," someone joked.

Suddenly, a veighl of mist desended.

"What is that?" Martin asked. There was a huge shadow in the mist.

"It's the yeti!" Sarah cried. "It picked up our sent."

b. Rewrite the incorrect words in **Question 5a** using the correct spellings.

_____   _____   _____

_____   _____   _____

_____   _____   _____

Tip Review the spelling patterns for tricky spellings in the **Remember** box to help.

Negative and opposite prefixes

Remember

When a prefix is added to the start of a word, it can give the new word a negative or opposite meaning. For example: 'friendly' and '**un**friendly' (negative meaning) or 'agree' and '**dis**agree' (opposite meaning). Do not change the spelling of the root or base word when adding the prefix.

 Practise

(1) Circle the word with the correct prefix for each definition.

    a. the negative of 'fortune'   disfortune   unfortune   misfortune

    b. the opposite of 'logical'   mislogical   illogical   delogical

    c. the negative of 'adequate'   inadequate   imadequate   iladequate

    d. the opposite of 'allow'   imallow   misallow   disallow

(2) Draw lines to match each prefix to the correct word. Use each prefix once.

non	climax
anti	mature
de	sense
im	code

Extend

(3) Rewrite these words with the correct prefix to give them a negative or opposite meaning.

    a. comfortable _____   **b.** regular _____

    c. qualification _____   **d.** social _____

(4) Add the correct prefix to each word. Use each prefix once.

> dis   mis   il   anti   in   de

a. _____judge   **b.** _____complete   **c.** _____obey

d. _____legal   **e.** _____frost   **f.** _____clockwise

Apply

(5) Write **four** sentences of your own using words that start with the prefixes in the box.

> il   ir   im   in

a. _____

b. _____

c. _____

d. _____

(6) Rewrite these sentences. Add the correct prefixes to the underlined words to give them a negative or opposite meaning.

The teacher said, "Your handwriting is <u>accurate</u> and <u>legible</u>. You have <u>understood</u> the task and used <u>appropriate</u> language. Your ideas are <u>logical</u> and your punctuation is <u>correct</u>."
"Does that mean you <u>like</u> it?" I asked <u>helpfully</u>.

_____

_____

_____

_____

Prefixes with different meanings

Remember

When a prefix is added to the start of a word, it gives the new word a different meaning. For example: the prefix sub– can be added to the word 'heading' to make the word '**sub**heading'.

Other prefixes include auto–, inter– and bi–. Do not change the spelling of the root or base word when adding the prefix.

Practise

1 Draw lines to match each prefix to the correct word. Use each prefix once.

over	city
bi	biography
auto	marine
sub	cycle
inter	take

Tip Think about the meaning of each prefix to decide which word it goes with.

2 Circle the word with the correct prefix for each definition.

a. a shape with three sides   biangle   uniangle   triangle

b. beyond the laws of nature   supernatural   subnatural   overnatural

c. to lower the price of   produce   reduce   introduce

d. protective clothing   underalls   superalls   overalls

e. a person's signature   telegraph   autograph   paragraph

⟫ Extend

3 Add the correct prefix to each word. Use each prefix once.

> inter   trans   sub   super   tri   under

a. _____ tract

b. _____ line

c. _____ fere

d. _____ dent

e. _____ power

f. _____ port

4 Add the correct prefix to the base word on the right to make the word with the meaning on the left.

a. to put under water   _____ merge

b. to change from one language to another   _____ late

c. to not give enough money   _____ pay

d. to go back somewhere   _____ turn

☁ Apply

5 Complete the words using the prefixes in the box so that the sentences make sense.

> tri   re   auto   inter   sub   under   aero   over

a. I would like you to _____ write this sentence to add a

_____ ordinate clause.

b. The _____ cover spy travelled _____ seas frequently on her

various missions.

c. An _____ plane is certainly much faster than an _____ mobile.

d. The young athlete was proud to have won the _____ athlon at the

_____ national competition.

The –tion, –sion, –ssion and –cian suffixes

Remember

A suffix is a letter string added to the end of a root word to make a new word with a different meaning. Sometimes the spelling of the root word changes when a suffix is added. For example: 'discuss' becomes 'discuss**ion**' (add –ion), but 'educate' becomes 'educat**ion**' (remove 'e' and add –ion). Words ending in –tion, –sion, –ssion and –cian all have the same sound at the end, so it is important to think about how they are spelt.

Practise

(1) **a.** Circle the words in the cloud with the correct –tion and –sion suffixes.

> injection   expansion   complesion
>
> acsion   tention   confusion   suggesion

b. Rewrite the incorrect words in **Question 1a** using the correct spellings.

_____   _____

_____   _____

(2) Underline the words with the correct –ssion or –cian suffix for each definition.

a. someone who performs magic tricks   magician   magission

b. a trip with a purpose   mician   mission

c. allowed to do something   permician   permission

d. someone who fixes electrical items   electrician   electrission

e. someone who runs the country   politician   politission

f. the look on your face   exprecian   expression

g. explaining that you are guilty   confecian   confession

Tip When you have finished this question, look at the definitions and your answers. Can you see a pattern for when you should use the –cian suffix?

Extend

3 Complete these suffix 'sums' by adding the suffix to the base word correctly.

a. invent + tion = _____

b. confuse + sion = _____

c. admit + ssion = _____

d. music + cian   = _____

e. attend + tion = _____

f. divide + sion   = _____

4 Draw lines to match each root or base word to the correct suffix, then write out the words in full.

infect		cian	_____
transmit		ssion	_____
extend		tion	_____
technic		sion	_____

Apply

5 a. Circle the **nine** incorrect spellings in this story.

> When I was young, I had an obsesion with illussions. I thought that being a
> magition would be a brilliant profesion. One day, I tried to perform a new
> vercian of a trick eating chillies. Unfortunately, I had a bad reactsion and
> terrible indigestcian. My eyes watered so much I had to go to the option.
> It was an easy decission to become a teacher instead!

b. Write the correct spellings of the misspelt words.

_____ _____ _____

_____ _____ _____

_____ _____ _____

Words ending 'sure', 'ture' and 'er'

Remember

Many words that rhyme with 'mea**sure**' and 'pic**ture**' end with 'sure' and 'ture' spellings. However, there are some exceptions. Root words that end with 'ch' or 'tch' and –er make the same sound as the 'ture' ending. For example: 'teach**er**'.

 Practise

1 **a.** Circle the words in the cloud with the correct 'sure' and 'ture' spellings.

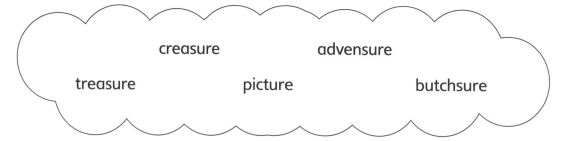

creasure   advensure

treasure   picture   butchsure

b. Rewrite the incorrect words in **Question 1a** using the correct spellings.

_____   _____   _____

2 Complete these words using the correct 'sure' or 'ture' ending.

a. depar_____   **b.** furni_____

c. na_____   **d.** enclo_____

 Extend

3 Draw lines to match each word beginning to the correct ending, then write the words out in full.

lei		ture	

_____

mix		er	

_____

preach		sure	

_____

4 Write the correct word from the box to complete each sentence. Use each word once.

> pressure   future   capture   culture   gesture

a. In _____, please tell me if you are going to do that.

b. London is a city famous for its _____.

c. Sending those flowers to your aunt was a thoughtful _____.

d. The _____ to perform the final dance in the show made Roya feel worried.

e. In the adventure story, the pirates _____ the unlucky sailors.

Apply

5 Write **five** sentences of your own using these 'ture' words. Use **one** word in each sentence.

> puncture   departure   mixture   fracture   adventure

a. _____

_____

b. _____

_____

c. _____

_____

d. _____

_____

e. _____

_____

Suffixes for changing verbs to nouns

Remember

When a suffix is added to a word, it can change the word meaning. It can also change the word class. For example: 'inform' is a verb but adding the suffix –ation makes the noun 'inform**ation**'.

Practise

1. Sort the words from the box into the Venn diagram. Decide if they are verbs or nouns. Some of the words can be both.

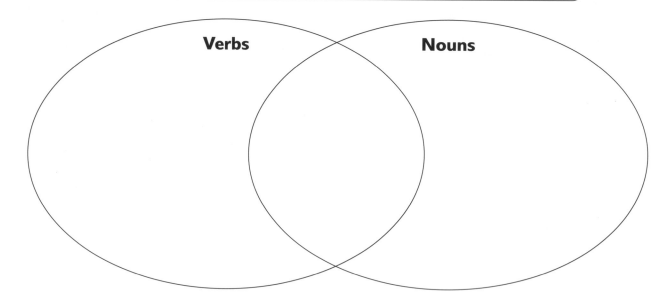

business   exercise   breathe   guard   separate

increase   century   library   possess

Verbs   **Nouns**

Extend

2. Change each verb into a noun by adding a –tion or –ation suffix.

Verb	Noun	Verb	Noun
a. direct		**b.** adopt	
c. form		**d.** consider	
e. educate		**f.** delete	

③ Change each noun into a verb by removing the –tion or –ation suffix.

Noun	Verb	Noun	Verb
a. selection		**b.** donation	
c. invention		**d.** pollution	
e. eruption		**f.** sensation	

Tip Some words might need some extra letters adding back on. Think about what letters you might take off to add a –tion or –ation suffix to a word.

Apply

④ Change each verb into a noun by adding a –tion or –ation suffix, then write **three** sentences of your own using the nouns. One has been done for you.

locate   add   create   act

a. __location__

After some research, the archaeologists found the most likely

location for the ruins of the old castle.

b. _____

_____

_____

c. _____

_____

_____

d. _____

_____

_____

Homophones and near homophones

 Practise

(1) Draw lines to match the homophones.

mist	fare
bury	piece
fair	missed
peace	berry

(2) Circle the correct homophones so that these sentences make sense.

a. Because of the **mist / missed**, we **mist / missed** the view of the mountains.

b. Jamal found a **berry / bury** and decided to **berry / bury** it in the flowerbed.

c. You must pay a **fair / fare** to go on a ride at the **fair / fare**.

d. The **piece / peace** and quiet was broken by a loud **piece / peace** of music.

 Extend

(3) Here are the definitions of two homophones. Write the correct homophone to match the definition.

a. A round metal disk on a ribbon that you get for winning. _____

b. When you interfere in something that is not your business. _____

4) Here are two homophones. Write the correct definition of each homophone.

a. grown _____

b. groan _____

Apply

5) Find all **five** pairs of homophones or near homophones in the word search. **One** word from each pair is given beside the word search. Write the other word in the homophone pair next to it when you have found it.

O	N	W	M	A	L	E	R
L	C	E	X	C	E	P	T
A	P	A	R	E	I	G	N
C	R	T	T	P	V	E	N
C	W	H	E	T	H	E	R
E	D	E	R	A	I	N	L
P	U	R	L	D	E	W	Y
T	E	J	M	A	I	L	B

a. except _____

b. whether _____

c. due _____

d. reign _____

e. mail _____

6) Complete these sentences using the **10** words from the word search. Use each word once.

a. The adult _____ butterfly sat on the grass, which was damp with

morning _____.

b. During the _____ of Charles I, people were able to post their

_____ for the first time.

c. _____ to the bad _____ forecast, the school fair

has been cancelled.

d. We _____ most types of rubbish for recycling,

_____ tins of paint.

e. We will go to the beach _____ it pours with _____

or not.

Alliteration

 Practise

1. Underline all of the words that begin with the same sound in these sentences.

   a. Nina tied nine knots in her napkin.

   b. Richie wrote a report about rare rabbits.

   c. Suddenly, Samira stood still in the centre of the circle.

   d. Karmen creates cute coats for koalas.

   e. One wet Wednesday we went to Weymouth.

   f. "Go and get that greedy goat," growled Guy.

2. Tick to show which sentences use alliteration. Tick **more than one**.

   There were forty-four fabulous pheasants. ☐

   I had a bumpy, lumpy duvet. ☐

   Soft snowflakes fell silently. ☐

   Please bring the string. ☐

≫ Extend

3. Write an adjective of your own that starts with the same sound as these nouns.

   a. _____ hedgehog   **b.** _____ sky

   c. _____ wind   **d.** _____ tiger

④ Complete these sentences using the words in the box to create alliteration. Use each word once.

> thieves   chewed   peaceful   nurse   licked   Katie

a. Chippy the chihuahua _____ some Cheddar cheese.

b. Theo met three thirsty _____ in a theatre.

c. Louise was _____ by Larry the lazy llama.

d. The playful painters picnicked in the _____ park.

e. The _____ knelt on his knobbly knees next to Nora.

f. Casper and _____ both caught colds at Christmas.

Tip The words should start with the same sound, but they may not always start with the same letter.

Apply

⑤ Write **five** sentences of your own using the sound in bold to create alliteration.

a. /t/ _____

_____

b. /f/ _____

_____

c. /b/ _____

_____

d. /c/ _____

_____

e. /n/ _____

_____

Personification

 Practise

1. Circle the noun phrase that is made to sound human in each sentence.

   a. The wind whispered through the wheat field.

   b. Jessie's alarm clock screamed in her ear.

   c. The stars in the sky winked at me.

   d. The garden was dressed up in a crisp, white suit.

2. What do you think the sentence in **Question 1d** means? Tick **one**.

   The garden was tidy. ☐

   The garden was wearing a suit. ☐

   The garden was covered in snow. ☐

   There was a white suit in the garden. ☐

3. Underline the verb that makes the noun phrase sound human in each sentence.

   a. The traffic lights refused to change to green.

   b. The setting sun bathed us in orange light.

   c. The gentle stream murmured over the pebbles.

   d. The cars bellowed at each other with their horns.

Tip A noun phrase is the noun itself and any other words used to modify it.

Extend

④ Draw lines to match each noun phrase to the personification that best completes the sentence.

The swimming pool	cried gently on to my window.
The lonely tree	danced on top of the candle.
The rain	was calling me to jump in.
The flame	peeked out from behind the clouds.
The moon	fought against the strong wind.

Apply

⑤ Complete these sentences using the verbs in the box to create personification.

> groaned   coughed   sleeps   held   ran   kissed

a. Grandad started the old engine, which rattled and then _____ into life.

b. To my surprise, a single snowflake appeared from nowhere and _____ me on the nose.

c. The terrible winter storm _____ the fishing boat in its teeth.

d. As the police officer sat down, the tiny chair _____ under him.

e. New York, which is in America, is famously known as the city that never _____.

f. Autumn leaves _____ around the empty playground like excited school children.

Year 4 word list

Remember

There is a list of words to learn in Years 3 and 4. The Year 4 word list includes a range of different word classes, such as nouns, adjectives, verbs and adverbs. Use these activities to practise some of the words.

Practise

1 Write these **12** words in alphabetical order.

century	accidentally	medicine	experience
guide	experiment	possession	address
position	mention	certain	grammar

a. _____   b. _____   c. _____

d. _____   e. _____   f. _____

g. _____   h. _____   i. _____

j. _____   k. _____   l. _____

2 Draw lines to match these words to their word class and meaning. One has been done for you.

heard	adjective	to rule as a king or queen
peculiar	noun	different to normal
reign	verb	one of four equal parts
breath	verb	detected using your ears
quarter	noun	air going into or out of your lungs

Tip Remember that you can use a dictionary to look up the definition of a word, which will help you find the word class.

⟫ Extend

③ Complete these sentences using the words in the box. Use each word once.

> calendar   purpose   separate   library
>
> therefore   material   ordinary   consider

a. The _____ of her trip was to visit the _____.

b. The detective examined the _____ thoroughly for something out

of the _____.

c. I lost my _____ and _____ missed the party.

d. To _____ a solid from a liquid, you should _____

using filter paper.

Apply

④ Look at the words in this word pyramid. Look up any words you do not know.

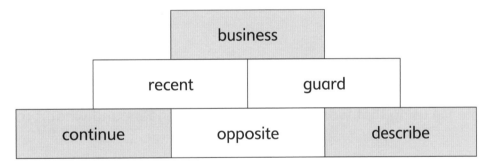

a. Write a sentence using **two** words from the shaded blocks.

_____

b. Write a sentence using **two** words from the unshaded blocks.

_____

c. Write a sentence using **three** words in the pyramid.

_____

_____

Thematic language

 ## Practise

1 **a.** Write the following verbs into the table, then use a dictionary to check the meaning of each word.

> quaff   writhe   wield   heave   clog   mope   wade   confiscate   preen

Words with meanings I know	Words with meanings I can guess	Words with meanings I don't know

b. Choose **one** word from the table with a meaning you didn't know. Write a sentence using that word to show you now understand what it means.

_____

_____

 ## Extend

2 Circle the word that is closest in meaning to the word in bold.

a. faint   bold   weak   soft

b. hoist   lift   lower   boost

c. current   flood   raisin   flow

d. scurry   dash   stroll   slip

3 Write the missing letters for each word using the meaning given in brackets as a clue.

a. d __ s __ ui __ e   (a way of hiding your identity)

b. po __ __ ess __ on   (something that you own)

c. c __ los __ a __   (extremely large)

d. __ __ wel __ ery   (necklaces, rings and bracelets)

Apply

4 Complete these sentences using the words in the box. Use each word once.

> suspect   obedient   accomplishment   protested

a. Her greatest _____ was to sail around the world on her own.

b. The police _____ that the thieves escaped in a stolen car.

c. Our dog is normally _____, but yesterday she stole the sausages from the barbecue.

d. Stuck in a traffic jam on the motorway, my baby brother _____ by crying loudly.

5 Write **three** sentences of your own using these adjectives. Use at least **one** adjective in each sentence.

> glistening   slender   unwise   glum   loyal   sour

a. _____

_____

b. _____

_____

c. _____

_____

Topic words

Remember

The vocabulary activities on these pages are linked to interesting topics across all subjects in the curriculum. Think about prefixes, suffixes and root words when working out the meanings of these words. A dictionary and thesaurus can be useful when coming across new words for the first time.

Practise

1. Sort these words into the subject that they would most likely be used in. Use a dictionary to help.

> ancient   estuary   magnify   armour   environment
>
> ceremony   graphite   delta   evidence

Science	History	Geography

Tip Although some words have been put in one topic here, you may find them helpful in lots of different topics. Pick the topic you use them in most.

Extend

2. Draw lines to match the start of each word to its ending and its meaning.

calli	fine	decorative writing using brushes or pens
con	graphy	a musical instrument you stretch and squeeze
con	dant	to keep someone or something in a limited space
pen	certina	a piece of jewellery that hangs around the neck

3 Write the missing letters to complete the words in these sentences.

a. Ensure you follow the in __ tr __ __ ti __ ns when carrying out your experiment.

b. The king ordered his favourite artist to paint a new p __ __ tr __ it of the queen.

c. The children o __ s __ rv __ d the ice changing to water.

d. The p __ ll __ __ ion in the river was making the citizens of the town sick.

Apply

4 Unscramble the letters in the underlined words, then rewrite the words with the correct spelling.

a. In past times, soldiers took part in <u>reychar</u> competitions to see who was the best shot.   _____

b. Sound is created by <u>bivatrions</u> travelling through a solid, liquid or gas.   _____

c. You can now recycle soft plastics such as sweet <u>warsprep</u> at the supermarket.   _____

d. The scientist invented a special <u>civede</u> to test for dangerous diseases.   _____

5 Complete these sentences using the words in the box. Use each word once.

| business | essay | scrutinised | cavity | furniture | repellent |

a. The geologist explored the huge _____ under the mountain.

b. My new coat is windproof and water _____.

c. You have no _____ interfering with my things.

d. The scientists _____ their investigation for any mistakes.

e. Items of _____ are usually made from wood, plastic or metal.

f. Martha wrote an _____ about the Amazon River.

The Iron Woman, by Ted Hughes

The Iron Woman is a book written by the author Ted Hughes, who also wrote *The Iron Man*. In this extract, just before dawn, Lucy encounters a giant creature covered in mud behind her house. Lucy tries to clean the giant creature using a watering hose, but she cannot wash away the mud.

At the same moment, still holding Lucy in her hand, the giant figure heaved upright. Lucy knew that the voice had rumbled, somewhere: "More water." She dropped the hose, which writhed itself into a comfortable position and went on squirting over the driveway.

"There's the canal," she said.

The other great hand pushed her gently, till she lay in the crook of the huge arm, like a very small doll. This was no time to bother about the mud or the smell of it. She saw the light of her own bedroom go past, slightly below her, the window still open, as the giant woman turned up the street.

When they reached the canal, and stood on the bridge looking down, Lucy suddenly felt guilty. For some reason, it was almost empty of water, as she had never seen it before. A long, black, oily puddle lay between slopes of drying grey mud. And embedded in the mud were rusty bicycle wheels, supermarket trolleys, bedsteads, prams, old refrigerators, washing machines, car batteries, even two or three old cars, along with hundreds of rusty, twisted odds and ends, tangles of wire, cans and bottles and plastic bags. They both stared for a while. Lucy felt she was seeing this place for the first time. It looked like a canal only when it was full of water. Now it was nearly empty, it was obviously a rubbish dump.

"The river," came the low, rumbling voice, vibrating Lucy's whole body where she lay.

The river ran behind a strip of woodland, a mile away across the fields. That was a strange ride for Lucy. The sun had risen and hung clear, a red ball. She could see a light on in a farmhouse. A flock of sheep and lambs poured wildly into a far corner. Any second she expected to hear a shout.

But they reached the strip of trees. And there was the river. It swirled past, cold and unfriendly in the early light. The hand set Lucy down among the weeds of the bank, and she watched amazed as the gigantic figure waded out into midstream, till the water bulged and bubbled past those thighs that were like the pillars of a bridge. There, in the middle of the river, the giant woman kneeled, bowed, and plunged under the surface. For a moment, a great mound of foaming water heaved up. Then the head and shoulders hoisted clear, glistening black, and plunged under again, like the launching of a ship. Waves slopped over the bank and soaked Lucy to the knees. For a few minutes, it was like a giant sea beast out there, rearing up and plunging back under, in a boiling of muddy water.

Then abruptly the huge woman levered herself upright and came ashore. All the mud had been washed from her body. She shone like black glass. But her great face seemed to writhe. As if in pain. She spat out water and a groan came rumbling from her.

"It's washed you," cried Lucy. "You're clean."

But the face went on trying to spit out water, even though it had no more water to spit.

"It burns!" Lucy heard. "It burns!" And the enormous jointed fingers, bunched into fists, rubbed and squeezed at her eyes.

Lucy could now see her clearly in full daylight. She gazed at the giant tubes of the limbs, the millions of rivets, the funny concertinas at the joints. It was hard to believe what she was seeing.

"Are you a robot?" she cried.

Perhaps, she thought, somebody far off is controlling this creature, from a panel of dials. Perhaps she's a sort of human-shaped submarine. Perhaps …

But the rumbling voice came up out of the ground, through Lucy's legs:

"I am not a robot," it said. "I am the real thing." [...] "I am Iron Woman."

"Iron Woman!" whispered Lucy, staring at her again.

"And you are wondering why I have come," the voice went on.

The Iron Woman, by Ted Hughes

1 Why does Lucy suggest going to the canal?

_____

_____

2 Why does Lucy feel guilty when they reach the canal?

_____

_____

3 Look at the paragraph beginning _When they reached the canal ..._ Find and copy a word from the text that means the same as 'stuck'.

_____

4 Why does Lucy expect to hear a shout?

_____

_____

5 Look at the paragraph beginning _But they reached the strip of trees ..._ Find and copy **four** verbs that describe how the Iron Woman moves.

a. _____

b. _____

c. _____

d. _____

6 Describe what the Iron Woman does in the river in your own words.

_____

_____

7 Why do you think the Iron Woman spits out the water and says it burns?

_____

_____

_____

8 The writer uses similes to say things look 'like' other things. Find and copy the noun phrases used to describe these things.

a. Lucy in the Iron Woman's arms ⟶ like _____

b. the Iron Woman's thighs ⟶ like _____

c. the Iron Woman's clean body ⟶ like _____

9 What does the Iron Woman look like to Lucy?

_____

10 *"And you are wondering why I have come,"* the voice went on.

Thinking about the whole extract, why do you think the Iron Woman has come? Tick **one**.

to wash the mud off her body ☐

to show Lucy some of the problems in the area ☐

to take Lucy away on an adventure ☐

to make people think about looking after nature ☐

Grammar in Action

She gazed at the giant tubes of the limbs, the millions of rivets, the funny concertinas at the joints.

Underline the **three** expanded noun phrases in this sentence (see page 12 for expanded noun phrases).

The River Nile, by Giles Clare

This non-fiction text is about one of the most famous rivers in the world. Many people only think of Egypt when they think of the Nile, but this mighty river has played an important part in the lives of people across many African countries for thousands of years.

An incredible distance

The River Nile is considered to be the longest river in the world. It flows over 4000 miles, all the way from Lake Victoria in central Africa to Egypt. That is further than flying from London to New York. It takes approximately three months for the water leaving Lake Victoria in Uganda to reach the Mediterranean Sea.

Quick fact

Although most rivers flow southwards, the Nile flows to the north.

The Nile in ancient times

Although Egypt is a hot, dry country with very little rainfall, those who live on the banks of the River Nile have prospered from its life-giving water for thousands of years. Every year, when the Nile flooded, it left behind a silt that turned the desert into lush, fertile soil, perfect for growing crops. As a result, a wealthy, powerful civilisation developed there approximately 5000 years ago. The ancient Egyptians called the river *Ar* or *Aur*, meaning 'black', as this was the colour of the silt left behind by the floods.

The Nile was at the centre of life in ancient Egypt. The ancient Egyptians developed ways of channelling water from the river so that they could produce more food and goods. They grew crops, such as cotton, wheat and papyrus, that could be stored or traded. They also used the water for drinking, bathing and transportation. Many of their gods and goddesses were linked to the river. They believed, for example, that the god Khnum ruled over the floods and determined how much silt would be left on the riverbanks.

The journey begins

Many people agree that the source of the River Nile is Lake Victoria, which is known in Kenya as *Nam Lolwe* (body of endless water). Lake Victoria may seem endless, and more like a sea than a lake, because it is the largest lake in Africa. Impressively, its shoreline passes through three different African countries: Kenya, Tanzania and Uganda. There are around 1000 islands on the lake, even though its average depth is a fairly shallow 40m. The lake has even run dry a few times since it formed nearly half a million years ago.

Wildlife

The River Nile supports a large amount of wildlife. Along its route are clawless otters, giant fish, soft-shell turtles and 30 species of snakes, of which half are poisonous. Perhaps the most famous and feared river resident is the Nile crocodile. A male Nile crocodile can grow up to five metres long and move at high speeds in water to ambush its prey. They have even been known to attack humans. The hippos there can be just as dangerous, with their huge canine teeth and incredible speed even on land. These huge mammals can be aggressive and unpredictable on land and on water.

Quick fact

The Nile perch is a species of freshwater fish that can grow up to two metres long and weigh as much as 200kg. It is so large it is called *giwan ruwa* in Hausa language, which means 'water elephant'!

Khartoum

The city of Khartoum is the capital of Sudan. It is located where the Blue Nile and the White Nile, the two main tributaries of the River Nile, meet. The point where two rivers meet is called the confluence. Here the two tributaries combine and form one river, which continues its journey through Egypt to the sea. Home to five million people, Khartoum is one of the major trading centres on the river.

The journey ends

The Nile fans out as it reaches the Mediterranean Sea to cover a huge area called the Nile Delta. The river splits again here into two branches, the Damietta and the Rosetta. Around half of the population of Egypt live on the Delta, where the soil is ideal for agriculture. It is a bird-spotter's paradise: hundreds of thousands of migrating birds stop over in the marshy lakes each year.

Quick fact

The river gets its name from the Greek *Neilos*, which means a valley or river valley.

Pollution

Nowadays, there are many factories along the river, pumping out wastewater. Local people can no longer drink water straight from the river as the chemicals and waste make it dangerous and unpleasant to drink. The pollution is also harming the river wildlife. This means the number of fish is falling, so it is more difficult for the fishermen who depend on the river to catch enough fish to survive.

The River Nile, by Giles Clare

1 How long is the River Nile?

_____

2 Why were the floods so important to the ancient Egyptians?

_____

_____

3 Look at the paragraph beginning *The Nile was at the centre of life* ... Which word is closest in meaning to 'decided'? Tick **one**.

prospered ☐

developed ☐

traded ☐

determined ☐

4 What is unusual about the direction the Nile flows in compared to other rivers?

_____

_____

5 Draw lines to match each name to its meaning.

Nam Lolwe	water elephant
Aur	body of endless water
giwan ruwa	river valley
Neilos	black

6 Read the section with the heading **Wildlife**. Name **three** types of dangerous animals that live by the river.

_____

7 What happens at the 'confluence' in Khartoum?

_____

_____

8 Why might you visit the Nile Delta if you like birds?

_____

_____

9 Do you think the fishermen are pleased that there are factories along the Nile? Explain your answer using evidence from the text.

_____

_____

10 Where does the Nile end its journey? Tick **one**.

Lake Victoria ☐

Rosetta ☐

Mediterranean Sea ☐

Damietta ☐

Spelling in Action

Find and copy the word in the **Quick fact** box about the Nile perch that contains an /ai/ sound spelt 'ei' (see page 24 for tricky spellings).

_____

I Asked the River, by Valerie Bloom

This poem by Valerie Bloom is written as a conversation. It uses lots of rhyming, repetition and personification to get its message across.

"Why do you run?" I asked the river,
"So fast I can't compete."
"I run," the river said, "because
I have some streams to meet."

"Where do you go?" I asked the river,
"And what do you do there?"
"I go to the valley," the river said,
"Where I wash the rushes' hair."

"Why do you sing?" I asked the river,
"Such a sweet and happy tune?"
"Because," the river smiled,
"I'm having lunch with the sea at noon."

"Why do you laugh?" I asked the river,
"You'll share the joke I suppose?"
"I woke the mountain," the river grinned,
"By tickling his toes."

Then the river shuddered, groaned and sighed,
The song of the streams and the laughter died,
And it whispered sadly, "I can't, I can't,"
As it limped along like an ancient aunt.

"Now why do you wait?" I asked the river,
"And why is your current so slow?"
"Something holds me back," it said.
Its voice was faint and low.

"And is that why you're getting small?
Is that why you sigh?"
"I sigh," the river said, "because
I know that soon I'll die."

"Why don't you fight for life?" I asked,
"You only foam and seethe."
"My lungs are clogged," the river moaned,
"And I can hardly breathe."

"Perhaps a rest," I told the river,
"Would help to clear your head."
"I cannot rest," the river said,
"There's garbage in my bed."

"What's this garbage," I asked, disturbed,
"Which is clogging up your sand?"
"Poisonous waste and wrappers like this,
Which just fell from your hand."

I Asked the River, by Valerie Bloom

(1) The poem is written using direct speech. Who or what are having the conversation? Tick **two**.

the stream ☐   the writer ☐   the valley ☐

the sea ☐   the mountain ☐   the river ☐

(2) Which of the two things you ticked in **Question 1** is faster in the first verse? Explain your answer using evidence from the poem.

_____

_____

(3) Which plants grow in the valley by the river?

_____

(4) Underline the **five** verbs in the fourth verse that use personification to make the river sound more human. One has been done for you.

"Why do you <u>laugh</u>?" I asked the river,

"You'll share the joke I suppose?"

"I woke the mountain," the river grinned,

"By tickling his toes."

(5) Why does the river slow down?

_____

(6) _As it limped along like an ancient aunt._

What does this line about the river include? Tick **more than one**.

simile ☐   onomatopoeia ☐

personification ☐   alliteration ☐

(7) Find and copy **one** word from the eighth verse that has the same meaning as the word in bold.

a. blocked _____

b. boil _____

(8) *"Poisonous waste and wrappers like this,*
Which just fell from your hand."

What do these lines suggest? Tick **one**.

People drop rubbish in the river on purpose. ☐

People are careless about littering. ☐

People don't realise how poisonous wrappers are. ☐

(9) The river's feelings change during the poem. Describe how the river is feeling in the first four verses compared to the final six verses.

a. In the first four verses, the river feels _____.

b. In the final six verses, the river feels _____.

(10) What is the overall message of this poem? Tick **one**.

Rivers get blocked up if people throw rubbish in them. ☐

Rivers are affected by what people do. ☐

Rivers are important, natural things that we must look after. ☐

Grammar in Action

Find and copy the **two** possessive pronouns in the sixth verse (see page 6 for possessive pronouns).

_____ and _____

The Peppermint Pig, by Nina Bawden

Poll, who is nine, lives with her family in a leafy part of London, UK. She has a comfortable life where 'nothing dreadful had ever happened ... nor seemed likely to'. However, one day, she hears something unusual.

Poll was the naughtiest one of the family and the dreadful thing happened on one of her naughty days; a dark day of thick, mustardy fog that had specks of grit in it she could taste on her tongue. Theo was not allowed out because of his delicate chest and by the time Poll got home from school she was already angry. She had been in a cold classroom all day, some of the time stuck in the corner with the Dunce's Cap on, made of green drawing paper and smelling of gum, while Mother and Theo had been cosy at home, sharing secrets. Poll loved Theo but she was jealous by nature and when she came coughing in from the fog, hands and feet cold as toads, and found him sitting on Mother's lap by the fire where she wanted to be, she wished he was dead. *She* was supposed to be the baby, wasn't she?

She was naughty at tea. Children were expected to behave well in those days and although Emily Greengrass was less strict in some ways than most mothers, she was firm about table manners. It was always, "Sit up straight." "Don't talk with your mouth full." "Elbows off the table, I won't tell you again."

That afternoon, Poll had to be told once too often. Her mother said, "I've had enough, my girl. Under the table!"

Poll didn't mind. She had eaten as much as she wanted – she always ate a great deal, very fast, unlike Theo who chewed every mouthful so slowly that Mother's fresh scones, crisp and warm from the oven and dripping with butter, might have been dry lumps of old cardboard – and with a good tea inside her it was pleasant under the table. The starched white cloth hung down almost to the floor, making a good, private place where she could behave as she liked and no one to see. The linoleum was brown and patterned in criss-cross stripes of a lighter shade. Poll thought these looked like little gates and, pretending to be a baby again, tried to push them open with her fingers. She spat on the floor and blew on the spit, to see the colours change in the bubble. There were spiders in the dusty underside of the table and she fetched one down and teased him by letting him run and then barring his way until she felt sorry and took off her shoe to give him a ride in it.

By this time she was yawning. Someone – George, probably, he was always kind to Poll when she was punished – had pushed a small green hassock under the table and she rested her head on it. She didn't go to sleep properly, just dozed off and on, listening to the voices above her head and watching the feet round the table through the furry fringe of her lashes: George's heavy shoes, Lily's neat, black buttoned boots, and her mother's slippers that had silver buckles in the shape of small roses.

She must have slept in the end because suddenly her father's boots were where George's had been and his voice was saying, "I am so sorry about this, Emily dear."

Poll was awake at once. Father usually said "Mother". But perhaps what startled her most was the tone of his voice which was hoarse and slow as if some of the gritty fog had got into his throat and stayed there.

He said, "Whoever took the money, I was in charge and must be responsible. I should have locked the safe up before I left the office to speak to my father."

"Oh, I knew he'd bring us all down one day," Mother said, and Poll wondered who she was talking about. Dad had said, my father. But Grandpa Greengrass was dead …

The Peppermint Pig, by Nina Bawden

1. Why is Theo not allowed to go outside?

   _____

   _____

2. Why was Poll jealous of Theo?

   _____

   _____

3. What is the full name of the children's mother?

   _____

4. Poll is punished at school and at home that day. What **two** punishments is she given?

   a. _____

   _____

   b. _____

   _____

5. Describe **one** way in which Poll and Theo are different.

   _____

   _____

   _____

6. What is the name of the material on the floor?

   _____

7 *There were spiders in the dusty underside of the table and she fetched one down and teased him by letting him run and then barring his way until she felt sorry and took off her shoe to give him a ride in it.*

What impression does this give you about Poll?

_____

_____

8 Who else is at the table for tea, apart from Poll, Theo and their mother?

a. _____

b. _____

9 What has happened at Poll's father's office?

_____

_____

_____

10 What startles Poll when she hears her father talking? Tick **two**.

He speaks in a strange way. ☐

He calls her mother 'Mother' instead of 'Emily'. ☐

She sees his boots instead of George's. ☐

He calls her mother 'Emily' instead of 'Mother'. ☐

Vocabulary in Action

... a dark day of thick, mustardy fog that had specks of grit in it she could taste on her tongue.

Underline the **two** examples of alliteration in this sentence (see page 38 for alliteration).

How Children Lived, by Chris and Melanie Rice

This non-fiction text is about two children called Ichiro and Giovanna who lived a long time ago. The text explains how different and similar their lives were when they were growing up.

Growing up in Tokugawa Japan

It is 1650 in Japan. Ichiro is training to be a samurai like his father. One day he will fight for his overlord, the Tokugawa Shogun. He must also learn to write, dance, and play music, and to be polite and honourable. Above all, he must be loyal and obedient to the Shogun.

Ichiro

Ichiro wears a kimono. He has a pair of samurai trousers called *hakama*, which he wears over the kimono.

Life in Edo

Ichiro lives near the Shogun's castle in Edo (now called Tokyo), the capital city of Japan. The castle is surrounded by a moat. Most of the houses in Edo have walls made of paper and wood.

Japanese calligraphy

Ichiro is learning the art of Japanese calligraphy – a style of writing that is painted with a brush and ink.

Poetry

Poetry is also part of a samurai's training. Ichiro and his sisters like to read and write poetry in the rock garden at the side of their house.

Learning from the masters

Ichiro and his friends often go to watch some of the master samurai practising their skills at fighting. The samurai use both hands to wield their long, heavy swords, or *katana*. They also carry a short sword called a *wakizashi*.

Samurai armour

Ichiro admires the fine armour of the samurai. It is made of tough strips of leather or iron, which hang from the body on strings. A *kabuto*, or helmet, protects the head and face.

Serving tea

Tea ceremonies are an important part of samurai social life. Ichiro's father serves green tea to his guests in small bowls.

Fighting

My sisters are being taught how to fight with a *naginata* – a long stick with a curved top.

Growing up in Renaissance Italy

It is 1490 in the city of Florence. Giovanna lives with her family in a large palace with many servants. She is learning all the accomplishments of a lady. Her father, Francesco, has paid an artist to paint portraits of his wife and three children.

Giovanna

Giovanna wears a long velvet dress with wide sleeves, a simple headdress, and a pendant round her neck.

Giovanna's home

Giovanna's father is a wealthy banker and runs his business from the palace, which is in the centre of Florence.

Giovanna's possessions

Giovanna's favourite possessions are her pendant, jewellery box, and printed book. Her father says that until recently books were handwritten.

Giovanna's education

Giovanna and her sister are taught at home by a tutor. They have learnt to sing, play musical instruments, write poetry, and read Latin. They are also being taught how to run a household.

The portrait

Giovanna sits for her portrait with her sister and her baby brother. She wears her new dress.

Giovanna's mother

The artist has already finished the portrait of Giovanna's mother. She is a fine singer and is shown holding a music book. Francesco is proud to show the picture to all his friends.

Furniture

Giovanna's baby brother has the same cradle that she slept in as a baby. Like the other furniture in the palace, it is decorated with beautiful carvings.

Table manners

As well as knives, we now have forks to eat with. Sometimes I still use my fingers by mistake.

Singing madrigals

Sometimes, after dinner, my sister and I sing a song called a 'madrigal' for my father's friends.

How Children Lived, by Chris and Melanie Rice

(1) Look at the paragraph beginning *It is 1650* ... Which word is closest in meaning to 'faithful'? Tick **one**.

polite ☐

honourable ☐

loyal ☐

obedient ☐

(2) What was Tokyo called when Ichiro lived there?

_____

(3) Complete these sentences using information from the text.

a. A samurai wears _____

_____.

b. A samurai carries _____

_____.

(4) Where exactly did Giovanna live?

_____

_____

(5) What was different about Giovanna's book compared to other books that had existed before?

_____

(6) What was special about the palace furniture?

_____

7 Who do you think were the most powerful people in Ichiro and Giovanna's lives?

Ichiro: _____

Giovanna: _____

8 What did girls learn to do in Japan but not in Italy?

_____

9 Write **two** things that both Ichiro and Giovanna learnt.

a. _____

b. _____

10 Draw lines to match each item to the correct child.

| jewellery box |
| kimono |
| pendant |
| calligraphy |
| tea bowl |
| fork |

Ichiro

Giovanna

Spelling in Action

They have learnt to sing, play musical instruments, <u>write</u> poetry, and <u>read</u> Latin.

Look at the **two** underlined words in this sentence from the text. Can you think of a homophone for each of these words (see page 36 for homophones)?

_____ and _____

The Madhatters, by Aoife Mannix

Aoife Mannix is a poet and writer. When she was eight years old, she moved to a different part of Dublin, Ireland. This poem was inspired by her new neighbours.

Next door live three old ladies.

They're sisters, well into their eighties,

but to us kids, they seem beyond time.

They like to ask me and my brother in for cakes on winter evenings.

They have no electricity so their front room remains continually

lost in the romance of candlelight.

There are stacks of newspapers, magazines everywhere.

Their faded yellow prints paw at us as we stand in the

semi darkness breathing the rustling of ancient books,

the faint whiff of ghosts.

The eldest sister Sara is confined to a wheelchair.

She spends her days sitting in the window

feeding the budgies she keeps in an enormous cage.

We love those birds, their greens and sudden darts of yellow.

She tells us stories of their adventures in Africa with such animation,

we're all transported there.

And as we eat the strange sweet squares of pink icing

and sip our orange squash, they promise us this is nothing.

That one day we'll have a proper tea party,

just like Alice in Wonderland, with hats and everything,

and there'll be magic teapots that can talk,

and a cat that never stops smiling,

and the budgies will don their tuxedos,

and they'll wear their ball gowns,

and my brother can sport his cowboy suit if he wants.

And we'll have an enormous birthday cake

shaped like an aeroplane that will zoom around the room,

and endless cups of tea that can refill themselves.

When we leave, my brother whispers to me,

"Do you think they really are witches?"

I reply, "It's hard to tell, we'll have to wait till

we get the invite."

The Madhatters, by Aoife Mannix

(1) How are the old ladies related?

_____

(2) Why do the old ladies use candles?

_____

(3) There are papers, magazines and books in the house. Why might it be difficult to read them? Use words from the poem to support your answer.

_____

(4) What kind of birds does Sara keep?

_____

(5) What colour are the birds? Circle **more than one**.

    yellow   pink   orange   green

(6) _She tells us stories of their adventures in Africa with such animation, we're all transported there._

What do these two lines mean? Tick **one**.

Sara and the children travel to Africa. ☐

Sara draws cartoons of Africa to show what it was like. ☐

Sara tells the children how she was transported to Africa. ☐

Sara's stories make the children feel as if they are in Africa. ☐

(7) What do the old ladies promise the children they will do one day?

_____

_____

8 Draw lines to match the objects to the correct actions.

a cat	that zooms around the room
magic teapots	that can refill themselves
cups of tea	that can talk
a birthday cake	that never stops smiling

9 *and they'll wear their ball gowns,*

Look at the third verse. Find and copy **two** more words that mean the same as 'wear'.

_____ and _____

10 Why do you think the poet's brother believes the old ladies might be witches? Give **two** reasons.

_____

_____

_____

_____

Vocabulary in Action

Draw lines to match these lines from the poem to the correct descriptions (see page 38 for alliteration and page 40 for personification).

Their faded yellow prints paw at us	alliteration
the strange sweet squares of pink icing	personification

Operation Gadgetman!, by Malorie Blackman

> This text is part of a novel called 'Operation Gadgetman!'. Beans calls her dad 'Gadgetman' as he is always coming up with brilliant inventions. One day he gives each of Beans's friends a spy kit, which they show off at school.

"Look, everyone! Look what Beans's dad gave us!" Ann preened. "Dead-brill spy kits!"

There was a huge crowd around them in seconds. Beans was almost trampled underfoot in the rush.

"Beans calls her dad 'Gadgetman'. That's his job – he invents things, gadgets," Louisa explained. "And he gave us these."

SNAP! SNAP! SNAP! SNAP!

The clasps on the black plastic briefcases sprung back.

"Oooohhhh!"

"Look at that ..."

"Wow!"

Even though Beans knew what was in the briefcases, she was still excited. Dad would have loved this reaction! She stood on a chair to peer over everyone else's heads.

"There's an instruction book here." Ann picked up the manual on top of everything else in the briefcase and turned a couple of pages. She began to read. "Gadgetman Spy Kit Contents List: Special two-way pencil, torch (batteries not included), mirror, tweezers, magnifying glass, notepad, evidence bags, black-and-white fingertip powder, fingerprint brush, TOP SECRET folder ..."

"Did your dad really make all that?" Stephen turned round to ask Beans.

Beans nodded, her face growing more and more warm. "Dad had the idea and he wrote the instruction book. That has things in it like secret codes, masks and disguises, following suspects, the proper way to take fingerprints and all kinds of other stuff. Then Dad sent his idea to a toy company and they put the whole lot together."

"What's a ... a special two-way pencil?" Jessica asked.

"Half of it is a normal graphite pencil," Beans explained. "The other half has got specially treated wax down the middle. When you write with the wax end it doesn't show up until you do special things to it. It's all in the instruction book."

"And are all the spy kits the same?" asked Stephen.

Beans nodded.

"Can I have one?" Stephen asked eagerly.

"And me ..."

"Me too …"

"I don't know if Dad's got any more," Beans said quickly.

No way did she want the whole class camping out in her front garden.

"Mr Conran said the kits are going to be on sale at the end of this month," Louisa called out over the noise of everyone in the class asking Beans for a spy kit.

"WHAT IS GOING ON IN HERE?" Mr Lark's voice boomed out from behind everyone, making them all jump. "Beatrice Conran! What are you doing standing on that chair? Would you stand on your chairs at home?" he asked.

Beans opened her mouth to say that she often did, but Mr Lark got in first.

"No, of course you wouldn't," he said, answering his own question. By this time everyone else had darted back to their own desks.

"Louisa, Ann, come to the front of the class – and bring those cases with you," Mr Lark ordered.

He pulled his glasses down to the end of his nose, the better to scrutinise everyone. Beans couldn't be sure which glinted more, his piggy eyes or his snooker-ball bald patch, which went from the top of his forehead practically all the way back to his nape. She hated geography.

"It's a spy kit, sir," Louisa explained.

"Don't be facetious, child!" Mr Lark snapped.

When he saw what was in the cases Mr Lark said, "Right then! These are confiscated until the end of school. And you two will stay behind in detention for an hour this afternoon and write me an essay, entitled 'Why I was unwise to bring my toys to school'."

"Oh, but, sir …" Ann began.

"No buts." Mr Lark raised a hand. "Or you can both stay behind on Monday afternoon as well."

Ann shut up.

"But sir, it's Friday," Beans protested on her friends' behalf. "We all had things planned …"

"Then you'll just have to *un*plan them, won't you," Mr Lark retorted. "And as you're so concerned about your friends, Beatrice Conran, you can stay behind with them this afternoon. Your essay will be entitled 'Why I should not stand on school chairs'."

Beans's mouth fell open.

Operation Gadgetman!, by Malorie Blackman

(1) Find and copy **one** noun phrase that describes what the spy kits are found in.

_____

(2) Name **three** objects in the spy kits that are used to look at things.

a. _____

b. _____

c. _____

(3) What is special about how the pencil works? Explain your answer.

_____

_____

_____

(4) How do the children in the class react to the spy kits? Explain your answer using evidence from the text.

_____

_____

_____

(5) *Beans nodded, her face growing more and more warm.*

How does Beans feel about how her classmates react to the spy kits? Tick **one**.

ill ☐

angry ☐

proud ☐

hot ☐

6 What is Beans's real first name?

_____

7 Look at the paragraph beginning _He pulled his glasses down ..._
Find and copy **one** word that means the same as 'examine closely'.

_____

8 Why does Beans hate geography?

_____

_____

9 What **two** punishments does Mr Lark give Ann and Louisa?

a. _____

b. _____

10 _Beans's mouth fell open._
How do you think Beans feels about her punishment? Explain your answer.

_____

_____

_____

_____

Punctuation in Action

"Beans calls her dad 'Gadgetman'. That's his job – he invents things, gadgets," Louisa explained. "And he gave us these."

Underline all the words that are spoken in this direct speech (see page 18 for inverted commas).

Spy Science, by Jim Wiese

This non-fiction text is about spies. It contains some fun ideas for spying activities and how to do them. It also explains the science behind how the activities work.

Key pictures

You are a spy working under cover. You have figured out a way to obtain the key to a locked room, but must return it in a short time. You want to make a quick copy of the key so you can explore the room at a later time. What can you do? Try the following activity to see how it can be done.

Materials

- sheet of black construction paper
- key
- 4 rocks
- clock or watch

Procedure

Note: This activity must be performed outdoors on a sunny day.

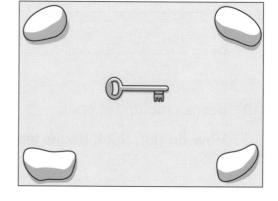

1   Place the construction paper in an open area in bright sunlight. Place a rock on each corner of the paper so that the wind will not blow it away.

2   Place the key in the centre of the paper.

3   Leave the project in the sun for at least four hours.

4   Remove the key and observe the paper. What do you see?

Explanation

Paper is made from wood **fibres** (slender threadlike structures that give woody plants strength) that have been pressed together. Construction paper gets its colour from different dyes. [...]

All coloured paper will eventually fade if exposed to sunlight. You may have noticed this on the bulletin board at school. Areas that have been covered with pictures are darker coloured than the surrounding areas when the pictures are removed.

Coloured paper fades even more quickly in direct sunlight. Black construction paper in particular fades very fast, because it contains the most dyes. The key, or any other object, blocks the sun and keeps the area under it from fading. After a short time, the rest of the paper fades, leaving an exact imprint of the key on the paper. You then have a picture of the key. An experienced spy could make a copy of the key and return the key to the locked room later.

Listening in

You're spying on two people in the next room. They're discussing their next operation, but you can't hear what they are saying. Try the following activity to make a device to hear through the doors.

Materials

- yardstick (metrestick)
- drinking glass
- 2 helpers

Procedure

1   Meet with the helpers in a room of your house. Tell them that you are going to try to listen to what they are saying from the next room. Ask them to have a conversation in normal tones of voice, no louder or softer than usual.

2   Have your helpers stand 2 yards (2m) away, facing the door. Leave the room and close the door.

3   Listen to the conversation. What do you hear?

4   Place the open end of the glass against the door, and place your ear against the bottom of the glass. What do you hear?

More fun stuff to do

With the glass against the door, have your helpers talk louder, then softer. Can you hear them both times?

Explanation

Every sound you hear, including speech, is caused by vibrations. When we speak, air from our lungs rushes past the vocal cords in our throats, causing them to **vibrate** (move to and fro repeatedly). These vibrations, like all vibrations, travel through air as sound waves. Sound waves can travel through all matter – gases, liquids, and solids. In this activity, the sound waves from the voices travel through the air to the door, then through the door itself. The sound waves then become sounds you can recognise with your ears.

You hear the voices better when you place a glass to the door, because the glass acts as a cavity to **amplify** (make louder) the sound. The sound waves inside the glass cavity hit the walls of the glass, reflect back, and reinforce each other in a process called **resonance**.

Spy Science, by Jim Wiese

(1) Why must the **Key pictures** activity be performed on a sunny day?

_____

_____

(2) Why do you need a clock or watch for the **Key pictures** activity?

_____

_____

_____

(3) Which of these subheadings could be replaced by the word **Instructions**? Tick **one**.

Materials ☐

Procedure ☐

Explanation ☐

(4) How is coloured paper made?

_____

_____

(5) Why does the paper under the key not fade?

_____

_____

(6) Why does black construction paper fade faster than other colours?

_____

_____

7 Which statement best describes how the human voice works? Tick **one**.

Our vocal cords push air to our lungs making them vibrate. ☐

Our lungs make sound waves by vibrating. ☐

Our vocal cords vibrate when our lungs push air past them. ☐

8 Tick to show whether each of these statements is true or false.

Statement	True	False
Sound travels through air.		
Sound travels through air and solids.		
Sound travels through air but not solids or liquids.		
Sound travels through air, solids and liquids.		

9 The **Listening in** activity suggests you listen to the conversation without a glass for the first time. Why?

_____

_____

10 How does a glass help to make voices louder? Explain your answer using technical words from the text.

_____

_____

_____

Spelling in Action

Find a word in the final paragraph that begins with the prefix re– which means 'to make stronger' (see page 28 for prefixes).

_____

Comparing texts: understanding feelings

These two poems feature different objects. A Russian doll is a set of wooden dolls that get smaller and are put inside each other. A strong box is a chest used for locking away important things. The two poems share a common theme about keeping feelings and thoughts hidden inside.

Then Laugh, by Bertha Adams Backus

Build for yourself a strong box,

Fashion each part with care;

When it's strong as your hand can make it,

Put all your troubles there;

Hide there all thought of your failures,

And each bitter cup that you quaff;

Lock all your heartaches within it,

Then sit on the lid and laugh.

Tell no one else its contents,

Never its secrets share;

When you've dropped in your care and worry

Keep them forever there;

Hide them from sight so completely

That the world will never dream half;

Fasten the strong box securely –

Then sit on the lid and laugh.

Russian Doll, by Rachel Rooney

All you see is outside me: my painted smile,
the rosy-posy shell, the fluttery eyes.
A butter-won't-melt-in-my-mouth-type me.

But inside there's another me, bored till playtime.
The wasting paper, daytime dreamer.
A can't-be-bothered-sort-of me.

And inside there's another me, full of cheek.
The quick, slick joker with a poking tongue.
A class-clown-funny-one-of me.

And inside there's another me who's smaller, scared.
The scurrying, worrying, yes miss whisperer.
A wouldn't-say-boo-to-a-goosey me.

And inside there's another me, all cross and bothered.
The scowling hot-head, stamping feet.
A didn't-do-it-blameless me.

And inside there's another me, forever jealous,
who never gets enough, compared.
A grass-is-always-greener me.

And deepest down, kept secretly,
a tiny, solid skittle doll.
The girl that hides inside of me.

Comparing texts: understanding feelings

(1) Look at 'Then Laugh'. List **three** things the poet suggests you should lock up in a strong box.

_____

(2) Look at the first verse of 'Then Laugh'. Find and copy a word that means the same as 'drink'.

_____

(3) In 'Then Laugh', the poet is giving the reader some advice about dealing with problems. Do you think it is good advice? Explain your answer.

_____

_____

(4) *Never its secrets share;*

These words are in an unusual order. Why do you think the poet uses this unusual word order?

_____

(5) In 'Russian Doll', what is the difference between the poet's 'outside me' and the other versions of her?

_____

_____

(6) Draw lines to match the underlined adjectives in these expanded noun phrases to their meanings.

The <u>scurrying</u>, worrying, yes miss whisperer	frowning
The <u>scowling</u> hot-head	hard
A tiny, <u>solid</u> skittle doll	rushing

7 Look at the second and fifth verses. What is the difference in meaning between 'can't-be-bothered' and 'all cross and bothered'?

_____

_____

8 The poet uses some expressions based on idioms to describe herself. Find them in the poem and draw lines to match them to their meanings.

A wouldn't-say-boo-to-a-goosey me	someone who always wants more
A grass-is-always-greener me	someone who appears to be innocent
A butter-won't-melt-in-my-mouth-type me	someone who is very shy

9 Why do you think the poem is called 'Russian Doll'?

_____

_____

10 Which statement best describes the theme of **both** poems? Tick **one**.

Everyone is different. ☐

Everyone has hidden feelings. ☐

Everyone has worries. ☐

Grammar in Action

Look at the first two lines of 'Then Laugh'. Find and copy **two** determiners (see page 8 for determiners).

_____ and _____

Writing skills: Spy Secrets

The Writing skills task is inspired by the themes in the reading comprehension texts. It provides an opportunity to apply the skills practised in this book. Answer guidance can be downloaded from the **Schofield & Sims** website.

Imagine someone you know has a secret. Maybe your grandad is really a cunning spy, or your aunt is a notorious jewel thief. One day, you discover their special secret! Write a short story about the day you find out. Think about where you are, what time of day it is and how you feel. Include some dialogue between yourself and the person whose secret you have discovered. Use the prompt below to begin your story if you wish to.

You could use some of the following in your short story:

- paragraphs to organise events and dialogue (page 14)
- inverted commas (page 18)
- alliteration (page 38)
- personification (page 40).

Re-read 'Spy Science' (page 76) for some ideas.

"You? You!" I exclaimed in shock. "I can't believe it!"

_____

_____

_____

_____

_____

_____

_____

_____

_____

_____

Tip Remember to proofread your story and correct any missing punctuation and spelling mistakes.

Final practice

The Final practice includes grammar, punctuation, spelling, vocabulary and reading comprehension questions. Work through the questions carefully and try to answer each one. The target time for completing these questions is 45 minutes. The answers can be downloaded from the **Schofield & Sims** website.

(1) Underline the expanded noun phrase in this sentence.

Mumtaz rode to school on an old, tiny bicycle with colourful, flashing lights.

1 mark

(2) Tick to show which sentences use an apostrophe to show possession correctly. Tick **two**.

Do you know where the babys' blanket is? ☐

Michael has lost his' pocket money again. ☐

We were invited to see James's collection of miniature ships. ☐

The children's toys were spread all over the carpet. ☐

1 mark

(3) Insert **two** commas in the correct places in this sentence.

In the morning while I was cooking a vegetable curry a pigeon flew into the sitting room.

1 mark

(4) Tick to show whether each sentence uses alliteration, personification or both.

Sentence	Alliteration	Personification
a. That last biscuit is calling my name.		
b. One windy weekend we walked to Wimbledon.		
c. The shimmering, silver stars smiled down at the sparkling sea.		

1 mark

Final practice

5 Rewrite this sentence using the correct spellings of the underlined words.

One of my <u>neybours</u> pulled a <u>musle</u> playing football in the Sunday <u>leag</u>.

_____

_____

1 mark

6 Tick to show where the missing inverted commas should go. Tick **two**.

☐　　☐　　☐☐

"Ten past five, said Heather with a gasp. Oh no! It can't be time to go."

1 mark

7 Write the correct negative prefix for each word.

a. _____ logical

b. _____ patient

c. _____ correct

1 mark

8 Circle the determiner in this sentence. Underline the possessive pronoun.

Some jokes are terrible but not mine!

1 mark

9 Add the correct prefix to the base or root word on the right to make the word with the meaning on the left.

a. an underground railway system　　　_____ way

b. a four-sided shape　　　_____ rilateral

c. someone who changes words
into a different language　　　_____ lator

d. clothes worn beneath other clothes　　　_____ wear

1 mark

10 Underline the correct spellings in this sentence.

The **electrician / electrition** asked for **permision / permission** to

show off his **invencian / invention**.

1 mark

(11) Rewrite this sentence in Standard English.

She don't want nobody knowing it's her birthday.

_____

1 mark

(12) Rewrite this sentence using pronouns instead of the underlined nouns or noun phrases.

When Mikey drove his new car, <u>Mikey</u> dented <u>his new car</u> on a post before <u>Mikey</u> had even left the garage.

_____

_____

1 mark

(13) Draw lines to match the start of each word to the correct word ending.

arch		ture
recap		sure
in		er

1 mark

(14) Rewrite this sentence with the adverbial at the beginning.

Eliza could see a city of gleaming skyscrapers in the far distance.

_____

_____

1 mark

(15) Write the missing letters for each word using the clue given in brackets.

a. cen __ __ __ __   (one hundred years)

b. __ __ __ __ __ dent   (something that happens by mistake)

c. __ __ dre __ __   (the name of where you live)

1 mark

Final practice

The Secret Garden, by Frances Hodgson Burnett

This text is from a classic children's book about an orphaned girl called Mary. She goes to live with her uncle at a manor house with a special private walled garden.

Mary skipped round all the gardens and round the orchard, resting every few minutes. At length she went to her own special walk and made up her mind to try if she could skip the whole length of it. It was a good long skip and she began slowly, but before she had gone half-way down the path she was so hot and breathless that she was obliged to stop. She did not mind much, because she had already counted up to thirty. She stopped with a little laugh of pleasure, and there, lo and behold, was the robin swaying on a long branch of ivy. He had followed her and he greeted her with a chirp. As Mary had skipped towards him she felt something heavy in her pocket strike against her at each jump, and when she saw the robin, she laughed again.

"You showed me where the key was yesterday," she said. "You ought to show me the door today; but I don't believe you know!"

The robin flew from his swinging spray of ivy on to the top of the wall and he opened his beak and sang a loud, lovely trill, merely to show off. Nothing in the world is quite as adorably lovely as a robin when he shows off – and they are nearly always doing it.

Mary Lennox had heard a great deal about Magic in her Ayah's stories, and she always said that what happened almost at that moment was Magic.

One of the nice little gusts of wind rushed down the walk, and it was a stronger one than the rest. It was strong enough to wave the branches of the trees, and it was more than strong enough to sway the trailing sprays of untrimmed ivy hanging from the wall. Mary had stepped close to the robin, and suddenly the gust of wind swung aside some loose ivy trails, and more suddenly still she jumped toward it and caught it in her hand. This she did because she had seen something under it – a round knob which had been covered by the leaves hanging over it. It was the knob of a door.

She put her hands under the leaves and began to pull and push them aside. Thick as the ivy hung, it nearly all was a loose and swinging curtain, though some had crept over wood and iron. Mary's heart began to thump and her hands to shake a little in her delight and excitement. The robin kept singing and twittering away and tilting his head on one side, as if he were as excited as she was. What was this under her hands which was square and made of iron and which her fingers found a hole in?

It was the lock of the door which had been closed ten years and she put her hand in her pocket, drew out the key and found it fitted the keyhole. She put the key in and turned it. It took two hands to do it, but it did turn.

And then she took a long breath and looked behind her up the long walk to see if anyone was coming. No one was coming. No one ever did come, it seemed, and she took another long breath, because she could not help it, and she held back the swinging curtain of ivy and pushed back the door which opened slowly – slowly.

Then she slipped through it, and shut it behind her, and stood with her back against it, looking about her and breathing quite fast with excitement, and wonder, and delight.

She was standing *inside* the secret garden.

Final practice

16 Why does Mary stop skipping?

_____

17 *... she felt something heavy in her pocket strike against her at each jump ...*

What is in Mary's pocket?

_____ 1 mark

18 Tick **one** word that means the same as 'branch'.

behold ☐

spray ☐

orchard ☐

trill ☐ 1 mark

19 What **two** things happen that help Mary find the doorknob?

a. _____

_____

b. _____

_____ 2 marks

20 Why does Mary have to use two hands to turn the key? Explain your answer using evidence from the text.

_____

_____

_____ 2 marks

Final practice

21 *... looked behind her up the long walk to see if anyone was coming ...*

Why do you think Mary checks to see if anyone was coming?

_____

1 mark

22 How do you think Mary is feeling in this text? Circle **one**.

curious   happy   worried   playful

1 mark

23 Number these events 1 to 4 to show the order in which they take place.

Mary enters the secret garden.   ____

Mary's Ayah tells her stories about magic.   ____

The robin sings on top of the wall.   ____

Mary skips along the path.   ____

2 marks

24 Tick to show whether each statement is true or false.

Statement	True	False
Mary couldn't open the door to the secret garden because of the ivy.		
Someone came up the long walk as Mary opened the door.		
Mary was excited to have found the secret garden.		

2 marks

25 What do you think Mary will do next? Explain your answer using evidence from the text.

_____

_____

2 marks

Total:

30 marks